BAROQUE KEYBOARD PIECES

BOOK III

Edited by Richard Jones

The Associated Board of the Royal Schools of Music

CONTENTS

INTRODUCTION

Baroque Keyboard Pieces is a graded anthology, in five books, of the keyboard music of the period 1600–1750. It offers, taken as a whole, a fairly representative selection of the forms, styles and composers of that period, and aims to show how the music can be played stylishly, whether on the piano or on old instruments. A further aim has been to include pieces that are tuneful and memorable in the hope that the task of learning them will be enjoyable as well as instructive. For the same reason each book contains well-known as well as unfamiliar pieces. On the other hand, minor composers are sometimes more liberally represented than the great names in order to spread the knowledge of much fine and under-played music. The order of contents within each book is very loosely chronological: the selected pieces are arranged in groups according to source, date and nationality. An editorial note at the end of each piece gives a brief account of the source and text, remarks on the composer and the form or type represented at its first appearance in the volume concerned, and assistance in specific matters of interpretation. A few more general notes on the interpretation of Baroque keyboard music are given here.

Baroque music, in general, contains fewer performance indications than the music of later periods, for a good deal was left to the taste and sensibility of the player. This area of freedom was limited by the requirements of the *style* in which the music was written: hence we talk of 'stylish' playing. Some acquaintance with the style of the period and with various associated performance conventions that were widely understood at the time is therefore a prerequisite of effective interpretation. These matters are outlined briefly under the following headings.

Forms and Types The keyboard forms and types of the period vary in difficulty. For this reason the earlier books of this anthology contain predominantly keyboard dances, illustrative or character pieces, and preludes. The more difficult fugal, toccata and variation types occur with increasing frequency in the later books.

By far the most common form in the earlier books is *binary dance form*, which was almost universal in keyboard dances and often used on a larger scale in non-dance music, as in the Sonatas of Domenico Scarlatti or some of the Preludes from Bach's *Well-Tempered Clavier*. A binary piece is in two halves both of which are repeated. The first half often modulates to the dominant or relative major; the second half, known in French music as the *reprise*, returns to the tonic. *Rounded binary form*, in which the first strain is repeated at the close, eventually led to Classical sonata form (see Arne's Gavotte in B flat, Bk III, p.62). Longer binary pieces often have a *rhyming close:* the concluding sentence of the second half matches that of the first half, except in key. Compare, for example, the last six bars or so of each half of Mattheson's Air in A (Bk III, p.42). After both halves of a binary piece have been repeated, the closing sentence may be played again. This is known in French music as the *petite reprise*. It is usually indicated by the sign ✗ , as in Louis Couperin's Minuet in C (Bk II, p.12), but if the composer wishes to vary the sentence, he will write the repeat out in full: compare, for example, bb.17–24 and 25–32 of le Roux's Passepied in F (Bk II, p.26).

Binary dances are often combined in pairs of the same type — see Clérambault's Minuet I & II, for example (Bk II, p.27) — the second half being repeated after the first, giving rise to an overall ABA da capo structure. Or an alternating scheme may operate within one and the same piece, as in the French *rondeau* (Eng.: *Round O*), precursor of the Classical rondo, in which the first strain — the *rondeau* proper — acts as a refrain, alternating with a number of episodes or *couplets*, which may be in contrasting keys. The overall structure will thus be ABA, or ABACA, as in François Couperin's *Le Petit-Rien* (Bk II, p.50), or ABACADA and so on, depending on the number of episodes the composer chooses to include.

Tempo Baroque keyboard music contains comparatively few tempo marks. In keyboard dances the tempo depends on the characteristics of the type to which the dance belongs: *Bourrée*, *Gavotte*, *Minuet*, etc. These are discussed, in each volume of this anthology, at the first occurrence of the type concerned. Here, it is worth noting that the character of the various dance types did not remain static but evolved throughout the Baroque period. The original dance became more and more elaborate until it was transformed into a highly sophisticated work of art. Compare, for example, an early 17th-century Saraband by William Lawes (Bk I, p.10) with the final stage in the development of the dance as exemplified in Bach's E minor Partita, BWV 830. Increased elaboration had to be accommodated within a slower tempo. This explains why 17th-century dances are often faster than their 18th-century counterparts. When playing an Allemande by Purcell, for example (e.g. Bk III, p.22), one will adopt a brisker tempo and a lighter touch than in an Allemande by Bach or Couperin.

Pieces without dance titles may, nonetheless, belong to or resemble a particular dance type, and their tempo can be judged accordingly. Thus Dandrieu's *L'Agréable* (Bk I, p.58) is a Gavotte, and Clarke's *A Farewell* (Bk III, p.34) has the character of a Saraband. In illustrative pieces, whether or not dance-like, the tempo will depend on the expressive character or 'affect' of the piece. This will normally be indicated by the title, as in Rameau's *La Boiteuse* (Bk II, p.53) which, but for its name — 'The Lame Woman' — might be mistaken for a Gigue.

Where Italian tempo marks are present, it should be borne in mind that they refer primarily to the character of the piece rather than to its tempo. Thus *Allegro* denotes 'cheerfully' or 'lively' rather than fast, and *Adagio* 'at ease' rather than slow. The clearly marked differences of tempo now indicated by these terms did not then apply: an Andante and an Allegro might be similar in tempo but quite different in mood.

Dynamics 17th- and 18th-century keyboard instruments — the harpsichord, clavichord, virginals and spinet — can be played expressively by employing rubato and subtle variations of touch. But, except for the clavichord, they have very limited dynamic capabilities compared with the piano. To compensate for this deficiency, expressive equivalents of dynamics tend to be built into Baroque keyboard music by the composer. A rise and fall in pitch often has the same emotional effect as a dynamic rise and fall; notes at both extremes of the range can have a climactic effect; a full texture creates a *forte*, and a thin texture a *piano*; and the gradual addition of harmony notes can build a *crescendo*, their reduction a *diminuendo*. The two-manual harpsichord adds the further possibility of large-scale structural dynamics: the lower manual can be treated as equivalent to *forte*, and the upper to *piano*, while a *mezzo forte* can be achieved by playing with one hand on the upper manual and the other on the lower.

When transferring harpsichord music to the piano, real dynamics can be used where only the suggestion of their effect was possible on the harpsichord. The possibilities of expressive dynamic inflection available on the piano should be used to the full. But broader dynamic contrasts should be used sparingly and only where clearly warranted in the music. In binary pieces, for example, many of which will have been conceived with a single-manual instrument in mind, variety is to be achieved mainly by varying the repeats rather than by introducing sharp dynamic contrasts. On the other hand, such contrasts are often effective in the case of pairs of dances that are to be played *alternativement* (alternately): Böhm's Rigaudon-Trio-Rigaudon (Bk III, p.26), for example, might be played, broadly speaking, *forte-piano-forte*. And the scheme ABACA in the *rondeau* — the alternating theme and episodes — might be played *f p f p f* (or a more sophisticated dynamic scheme might be adopted, depending on the character of the episodes).

Ornamentation Ornaments are an essential ingredient of Baroque keyboard music, adorning the melody in an expressive piece and adding rhythmic sparkle in a more lively one. To omit them altogether would be to rob the music of much of its charm and vitality. On the contrary, where few ornaments, or none at all, are present in the text, the contemporary player would have been expected to improvise them. However, it is often possible to be selective and flexible in one's approach to ornaments. And this attitude is always greatly preferable to being so deterred by the profuseness of the ornamentation, particularly in French music, as not to play the music at all. The recommended approach is to learn the music without the ornaments first, then add the essential ones — cadential shakes, and ornaments without which the melody sounds incomplete or impoverished — treating the remainder as optional, or reserving them for the repeats. Ornaments should be practised very slowly at first. Long shakes that enhance an expressive melody should be played with a certain rubato, a slight acceleration into the repercussions. Ornaments that add rhythmic life should be fast, crisp, even and accented.

Many different signs were used for one and the same ornament during the Baroque period. The original signs have been retained in this anthology — for it is important to grow accustomed to them — and an editorial explanation is given alongside them. As an aid to the elucidation of the signs, the tables of ornaments that many Baroque composers included in their keyboard publications are valuable as far as they go, but they do not show the many local variations of treatment that are necessary according to the specific context in which the ornament is placed. Here musical imagination and sensitiveness come into play, coupled with a respect for historical knowledge and accuracy. Many examples of a suggested variety of execution will be found in the course of this anthology. Here, a few more general points should be made.

The speed and number of repercussions of a shake will depend on the length of the note and the tempo. In the early 17th century, shakes more often begin on the main note; in the late 17th and 18th century, on the note above. But this decision, too, depends partly on context. Upper-note shakes (Ex. a) are, in effect, accented and appoggiatura-like. Where this effect is undesirable, as in the case of legato (b), fast tempo (c) or repeated notes (d), a main-note shake may be preferable.

(a) [musical example] (b) [musical example]
cf. [musical example]
(c) [musical example] (d) [musical example]
or [musical example]

Similarly on-the-beat ornaments are, in the mid and late Baroque, more common than before- and between-beat ornaments, but there is no doubt that in certain contexts the less usual alternatives are intended. Thus:

(a) [musical example] but (b) [musical example]

The question where the accent falls is, again, crucial. In (a) the main note, and therefore also the appoggiatura that replaces it, is accented; in (b) neither is accented.

Touch In early keyboard music, unlike that of the 19th century, a *non legato* touch is best regarded as the norm, and *legato* as only one among several different possibilities. The type of touch required is not necessarily indicated by the composer. Thus [notes] might, more often than not, be played thus: [notes]; but it could also be played staccato — [notes], staccatissimo — [notes], legato — [notes], or legatissimo — [notes].

The last-named type of touch — in effect, overlapping — is much more effective than plain legato in achieving a convincing *cantabile* on the harpsichord and can be usefully transferred to the piano. It is recommended by Rameau in the execution of appoggiaturas, in which it is essential to avoid any perceptible break between the grace-note and its resolution: [notes] (i.e.  [notes]) = [notes].

Articulation In executing a melodic line, a considerable variety of touch is desirable. By varying the touch, the player *articulates* the phrase; that is to say, joins some notes and separates others. Articulation is the most effective way of characterizing a piece in accordance with the intended 'affect' or expressive character. The decision whether to hold or release the keys, whether to join or separate the notes, will depend to a large extent on the accentuation of the passage concerned. Stressed notes should often be held or slurred, and unstressed notes shortened. And an accent is best achieved not by force but by shortening the previous note. Loeillet's Minuet in A (Bk III, p.58), for example, begins (omitting the ornaments):

[musical notation example]

In bb.1 & 3 the accent is on the 2nd beat of the bar; in bb.2 & 4 on the 1st beat. This can be clarified by the following articulation:

[musical notation example]

In the original, Loeillet's shakes and mordents further underline the accentuation.

Short slurred groups are, in Baroque music, far more common than long undifferentiated stretches of legato. In practice, a slurred pair or group of notes should be clearly set off from its surroundings by shortening the last note: thus [notation] = [notation]. The effect of a slur can be further marked by accenting the first note and then gradually reducing the tone. Appoggiaturas should invariably be played in this way, whether written out in full or notated as ornaments: thus [notation] = [notation]. The accent sign here indicates a slight increase in the velocity with which the finger strikes the key, not a muscular show of force. Applying these principles to Greene's Andante in A (Bk II, p.63), which, omitting a mordent on the 9th note, begins thus:

(the first crotchet in the 2nd bar forms a written-out appoggiatura), we arrive at:

Rhythm The notation of rhythm is often only approximate in Baroque music. The task of bringing it to life by imparting grace or vitality (depending on the context) to the notated rhythms is left in the hands of the performer. This often means employing various forms of rubato. One of the most common of these is *inequality* or *notes inégales*: the unequal playing of notes that are notated as equal in length. Typically, flowing quavers or semi-quavers are played with a very slight long-short lilt; thus, very approximately, [notation] = [notation]. Since unequal playing is designed to enhance the grace and elegance of a melody, it is confined to mainly conjunct, melodic notes; largely disjunct or broken-chordal notes should remain equal. If notes are slurred in pairs — [notation] or [notation] — the inequality is reversed so that the notes are played in short-long groups ([notation] or [notation]): the so-called Scotch Snap or Lombardic rhythm. The degree of inequality adopted is a matter of taste, varying from one piece to another — it will clearly be more pronounced in vigorous pieces, less so in expressive ones — and even within a piece. *Notes inégales* belong primarily to French music but are by no means confined to it: they became common practice in England after the Restoration and should no doubt often be applied in German music written — as is frequently the case — in the French style.

A related convention is *the variable value of the dot*. Rhythms notated unequally may be, in practice, more or less unequal than written, depending on the intended effect. Thus [notation] may either be played as written (perhaps modified to [notation] in more vigorous passages) or softened to [notation]. And [notation] may be sharpened to [notation] or [notation]. The increased vigour of sharpened dotted rhythms is useful not only in lively pieces but in slow ones, such as Sarabands, in which the rhythm would otherwise sound sluggish.

It is often necessary to *assimilate* variously notated rhythms to the prevailing rhythm of a piece. Thus in many cases *all* the rhythms of a piece should be dotted, despite the fact that only some of them are thus notated. Here are some examples of rhythmic assimilation:

(a) [notation] = [notation]

(b) [notation] = [notation]

(c) [notation] = [notation]

In Ex. (a) the quaver rhythm of the 1st beat is assimilated to the dotted quaver rhythm of the 2nd. In (b) the dotted crotchet rhythm of the upper part falls in line with the dotted quaver rhythm of the lower. And in (c) the dotted rhythms of one part are adjusted to the triplet rhythms of the other.

One further rhythmic characteristic of Baroque music should be mentioned here briefly, namely *hemiola* rhythm. Triple-time pieces often include a pair of bars that are to be played as if they were notated as three bars of duple time. The passage must be articulated in such a way that the temporary change of metre is made absolutely clear. In this anthology, hemiola is shown by square brackets, as in this example from Fischer's Minuet in A minor (Bk III, p.28):

which should be played thus:

Harmony Due to the characteristics of Baroque keyboard instruments, chordal passages and harmonic accompaniments are normally broken into more or less elaborate patterns in order to fill the texture, enrich the harmonic background, and preserve interest and vitality. The term *style brisé*, or 'broken style', though strictly speaking referring to the transference of lute figuration to 17th-century French harpsichord music, is often extended to cover this characteristic of Baroque keyboard textures in general. Here is a simple example from Dieupart's Passepied in D (Bk II, p.29). The bass and harmony of bb.1–4 are standard:

but instead of notating the chords thus, Dieupart indicates that they are to be broken and their notes sustained for the length of the bar:

This kind of texture, in which notes are struck frequently and, being sustained, overlap with one another, is ideally suited to the keyboard. And harmony in Baroque keyboard music, however notated, tends to gravitate towards it.

Thus chords notated as unbroken should often be spread or *arpeggiated*:

[notation] might be played [notation] or [notation]

Various signs are used to indicate arpeggiation, the most familiar of which is [sign], but it is often left to the player to decide how and where to arpeggiate chords. More elaborate forms of arpeggiation are frequent and may either be indicated by signs, as in the last bar of each strain of Rameau's *Le Lardon* (Bk II, p.52), or notated in full, as in the last two bars of Purcell's Prelude in C, Z.665/1 (Bk III, p.22). Examples such as these provide models for more elaborate extempore arpeggiation elsewhere. Arpeggiated chords can, further, be embellished by incorporating slides (Ex. a) and passing acciaccaturas (Ex. b; non-harmonic notes that are not sustained):

(a) [notation] = [notation]   (b) [notation] = [notation]

These ornaments would frequently have been added in performance, regardless of whether or not they were indicated by the composer.

Not only are chords notated as such often broken, but — conversely — the notes of broken-chordal figures are often sustained to build up chords. This may be indicated by slurs, as in bb.12 & 16 of Rameau's *La Boiteuse* (Bk II, p.53), or by double-stemming, as in the r.h. part of Dandrieu's *La Prévenante* (Bk II, p.54). But it is often left unnotated and has to be inferred from the character of the music. In *L'Amusante* (Bk III, p.56), Daquin assists the player by marking the l.h. quavers 'nottes très liées' ('notes very joined'):

should therefore be played thus:

Molto tenuto playing of this kind is a very common resource in harpsichord music and should be used in place of the sustaining pedal when Baroque keyboard music is transferred to the piano.

Fingering Our modern fingering methods have a tendency to encourage the continuous legato that is more appropriate to 19th-century keyboard music than to that of the Baroque period. To a certain extent, therefore, it is desirable to revive older fingering methods when playing the music of this period. Fingerings should be used that facilitate the possibilities on either side of legato: overlapping (as in *tenuto* and *legatissimo*) and separation (breaks between slurs and *non legato*). Changing fingers on held notes is particularly useful as a means of sustaining harmony notes, as in this example from Fischer's Minuet in F (Bk II, p.25):

Middle parts in a contrapuntal texture often have to be divided between the hands in order to maintain the same articulation at every occurrence of the theme — see, for example, the *Tastata* from Pasquini's Suite in G, bb.2–3 (Bk III, p.24). The use of the same finger on successive notes can force separation, either of single notes, as in Purcell's *Prelude for the fingering* (Bk I, p.21; see r.h., bb.8–14 and l.h., bb.5–6 and 10–13), which is fully fingered in the original, or of short phrases, as in Dieupart's Passepied in D (Bk II, p.29), bb.11–14:

Breaking a line into short slurred groups can be enforced by other forms of disjunct fingering, as in this example from Rameau's Minuet I in G (Bk III, p.53), bb.18–20 (treble only, ornaments omitted):

where the suggested fingering encourages the correct articulation of the suspension:

Placing long fingers over short (3 over 4; 3 or 4 over 5), as in

William Lawes's *Symphony*, bb.13–14 (Bk III, p.17), and lateral shifts of hand-position, as in Locke's Prelude in C, bb.15–16 (Bk II, p.16), are very useful older alternatives to thumb-under movements. The one method has the advantage that it turns the hand in the playing direction; the other, that it helps to maintain a quiescent hand.

Finally, avoid placing the short thumb and little finger on black notes wherever possible. And practice executing shakes and mordents on 4 3 and even 5 4, as well as on the more usual 3 2 and on alternate fingers.

EDITORIAL METHOD

Texts are based, for the most part, on the original editions, but occasionally on autographs (where extant) or early manuscript copies. The editorial aim has been to adhere as closely as possible to the composer's original text by transcribing directly from the best available sources and by keeping editorial alterations and additions to a minimum. Any editorial marks are, moreover, clearly differentiated as such. Suggestions for ornament realizations (at the first occurrence of a particular ornament in a specific context) and for phrasing and articulation, arpeggiation, and the application of rhythmic conventions are given either in words at the end of the piece or in small notation between the staves. Fingering, commas (showing breaks between phrases) and accidentals to ornaments are editorial unless otherwise stated. All other editorial marks are given in small print or square brackets, with the exception of words (italics; original words are roman), slurs and ties (⁀), indications of hemiola or other rhythmic displacements (⌐¬), allocation of notes to r.h. or l.h. (R/L or ⌈⌊), and the reminder that a note, being present simultaneously in another part, should not be struck (round brackets).

ACKNOWLEDGEMENTS

Most grateful thanks are due to the music departments of the following libraries for granting access to, or providing microfilms of, the manuscripts and first editions in their possession and for permitting their use as the sources of this anthology: Deutscher Staatsbibliothek, Berlin; Staatsbibliothek Preussischer Kulturbesitz, Berlin; The Fitzwilliam Museum, Cambridge; Hessische Landes- und Hochschulbibliothek, Darmstadt; Musikbibliothek der Stadt Leipzig; The British Library, London; The Bodleian Library, Oxford; and the Bibliothèque Nationale, Paris.

RICHARD D. P. JONES
Oxford, 1988

Corrente terza

Girolamo Frescobaldi
(1583–1643)

Frescobaldi was organist at St Peter's, Rome (1608–28 & 1634–43) and, for a shorter period (1628–34), at the Medici court in Florence. He was the most important Italian keyboard composer before Domenico Scarlatti.

The *Corrente* (literally 'running') is a fast dance in triple time: the Italian equivalent of the French *Courante*. Use lively phrasing that stresses the 1st beat of the bar, e.g. bb.1–4: ; bb.13 ff.: etc.; and bb. 24 ff.: etc.

The original contains no ornaments, but a contemporary player would have been expected to improvise them. An optional editorial scheme of ornaments is therefore given here. Note that shakes at this period more often than not begin on the main note.

Source: *Il primo Libro d'Intavolatura di Toccate di Cimbalo et Organo* (Rome, 1628). Key signature: one flat; time signature: c$\frac{3}{2}$; last chord: breves.

Corrente quarta

Girolamo Frescobaldi

The editorial ornamentation shows how a contemporary player might have embellished the piece. Note that the same sign – *t* – serves for both shakes and mordents, and that shakes usually begin on the main note. Suggested phrasing of bb.1–3: ♩ | ♩. ♪♪ | ♩. ♪♪ | ♩ ; and of bb.11 ff.: ♩ | ♩. ♪♪ | ♩ ♩ | ♩ ♩ ♩ | ♩♩♩♩♩ | ♩

Source: *Il primo Libro d'Intavolatura* (Rome, 1628). Key signature: one flat; time signature: C3; last chord: breves.

Sarabande
'Jeunes Zéphirs'

Jacques Champion de Chambonnières
(*c.* 1602–1672)

Chambonnières, harpsichordist to Louis XIII and Louis XIV, was founder of the French classical school of harpsichord playing and composition. He developed an idiomatic style based on the *style brisé* (broken or arpeggiated texture) of the French lutenists.

The *Saraband* (French: *Sarabande*) is a triple-time dance of Latin-American and Spanish origin. Sarabands of Chambonnières' time were, in general, somewhat faster than those of the early 18th century: moderate and graceful rather than slow and solemn. *Jeunes Zéphirs* (Young Zephyrs, or gentle breezes) illustrates the typical feminine cadences of the dance. And 1st-beat stresses (as in the figure ♩. ♪♩) frequently alternate with the 2nd-beat stresses (as in the figure ♩ ♩. ♪; to be phrased ♩ ♩. ♪) that later became a hallmark of the Saraband.

Suggested phrasing (bb.1–4): ♩. ♪♩ | ♩. ♪♩ | ♫♩ ♪ ♩ | ♩. ♫♩ |. The rhythm ♩. ♪ should be sharpened to ♩.. ♪, and quavers played in long–short pairs – ♫♫ = ♩ ♪♩ ♪ (see the discussion of *notes inégales* in the Introduction, p.6). Chambonnières' arpeggio sign (bb.7–9), when placed low down the chord, denotes upward spreading. 'Reprise' in b.9 means 'second half'. The final phrase, bb.25–8, constitutes a written-out *petite reprise*: an enhanced repeat of the previous phrase (bb.21–4), acting as a coda.

Players who are unaccustomed to the profuse ornamentation characteristic of French harpsichord music might, at first, omit all but the ornaments to the figures that first occur in bb.3–4, perhaps simplifying the interpretation of ♫♩ to ♫♫ and of ♩. ♫♩ to ♫♫♫.

Source: *Les Pièces de Clavessin*, Bk II (Paris, 1670). Time signature: 3. 1st ten. note of b.3: *c′* not *a*, but tie present.

Courante

Jacques Champion de Chambonnières

The French *Courante* is slower in tempo and more complex in rhythm and texture than the Italian *Corrente* (see above, p.8). Typically, the time oscillates between 3/2 (three minim beats) and 6/4 (two dotted minim beats), causing a deliberate sensation of rhythmic instability and, often, ambiguity.

In the noble opening phrase of this Courante, with its mixed major and minor harmony, the 3/2 of b.1 is immediately contradicted by the 6/4 of b.2, setting a rhythmic pattern for what follows. The equal crotchets in the r.h. of b.3 might be phrased ♩ ♩ ♩ ♩ ; and those of b.5: ♩ ♩ ♩ ♩ . The frequent dotted rhythms should be played ♩ ♩. ♪ and ♩ ♩. ♫ in order to throw the accent on to the dotted note.

In accordance with *notes inégales* (see Introduction, p.6), quavers should be played long-short; thus ♫♫ = ♩ ♪♪♪ . The cadential chords of bb.2, 8, 17 & 21 should be spread (up or down). In the bass | ♩ o | is a shorthand for | ♩ ♩ ♩ | (or | ♩ ♩. |). The ornamentation is throughout editorial.

Source: Bauyn MS. Time signature: 3; key signature: no flat.

Menuet de Poitou

Louis Couperin
(*c.* 1626–1661)

Double par M^r· Couperin

Louis Couperin, organist of St Gervais in Paris, was uncle of the more famous François Couperin and one of the most distinguished pupils of Chambonnières.

The *Minuet* (French: *Menuet*), a dance in moderate triple time, originated as a French country dance and was introduced to the court of Louis XIV in the mid-17th century. Louis Couperin's Minuets were thus written at a time when the dance type was new to art music, and when 3-bar phrases – as in the *Menuet de Poitou* – were not uncommon.

Mark the syncopations – ♩ ♩ – by shortening the previous note. The 1st strain might thus be phrased: ♩. ♪♪ | ♩ ♩ | ♩. ♫ | ♩. ♪♪ | ♩ ♩ ♩ | ♩. . All r.h. chords should be spread, perhaps upwards at the beginning of a phrase (e.g. b.1) and downwards at the end (e.g. b.6). Cadential chords might be spread in the rhythm ♫♩ , the chord in b.16 more slowly – ♫♩ – to fill an otherwise rather empty bar. The square brackets in bb.10–11 indicate hemiola rhythm; play as if one bar of 3/2 or three bars of 2/4: ♩. ♪♪ ♩ ♩ ♩. ♪ . The sign 𝄋 in b.13 indicates the *petite reprise*: the last six bars are to be played through again at the end, after the repeat of the 2nd half.

The *double*, or variation, might be used as a substitute for the repeats of the Minuet. Play the quavers as *notes inégales* (see Introduction, p.6): roughly ♩ ♪♪ ♩ ♪♪ ♪ .

Source: Bauyn MS (II, f. 68v; III, f. 53v). Time signature: 3. Double, b.3, bass: ♩· ♩· . The text given here is a conflation of the two source texts.

Menuet

Jean-Henri D'Anglebert
(1635–1691)

D'Anglebert, perhaps the finest of the 17th-century French *clavecinistes* (harpsichord players and composers) was, like Louis Couperin, a pupil of Chambonnières. In 1662 he succeeded his teacher as harpsichordist to Louis XIV.

In this Minuet the repeats are written out in full (bb.9–16 & 25–32), each strain having open (1st time) and closed (2nd time) endings. Of the many ornaments, the appoggiatura and shake to the figure ♩. ♬♩ and the long shake in the penultimate bar are essential. The remainder might be omitted at first and then added gradually as fluency in executing ornaments is acquired. The l.h. part illustrates the so-called *style brisé*: an idiomatic texture in which broken-chordal notes are sustained to create a rich harmonic background. In accordance with the convention of *notes inégales* (see Introduction, p.6), the quavers should be played in unequal pairs (approximately ♩ ♪♩ ♪).

Source: *Pièces de Clavecin* (Paris, 1689). Key signature: no sharp; time signature: 3; b.28: 𝆖 not 𝆗, but cf. b.20.

Symphony

William Lawes
(1602–1645)

William Lawes was younger brother of the composer Henry Lawes. He was a musician at the court of Charles I, served in the royalist army, and was killed in battle.

The term *Symphony* (Italian: *Sinfonia*) is here synonymous with 'prelude' or 'overture'. The l.h. part illustrates the 17th-century English equivalent of the French *style brisé* (broken or arpeggiated texture). The main interest is in the *cantabile* treble part, but at the 4th crotchet of b.9 and the 2nd of b.12 the bass leads in imitation at the 8ve. Spread the chords (perhaps downwards in the case of b.4, r.h.). Across the bar-line between bb.11 & 12, parallel 5ths between treble and tenor can be avoided by adding a passing acciaccatura to the r.h. chord:

Source: *Musicks Hand-maide* (London, 1663). Time signature: ₵; b.7b, 2nd treble note: dotted crotchet; ten.: ; bass: . The 1st time bars (bb.7a & 15a) and the ornaments are editorial.

Rant

Matthew Locke
(*c.* 1622–1677)

Matthew Locke was one of the most outstanding of Purcell's older contemporaries. He trained as a choir boy at Exeter Cathedral and became a court musician after the Restoration of 1660.

The *Rant* is a lively dance that demands vigorous phrasing; for example (bb.1–2): ♩ ♩ ♩ ♩. ♪♪ | ♩ ♩ ♩ ♩ . The syncopation in the r.h. of bb.2–4 etc. is marked by shortening the previous note: ♩ ♩ . The equal crotchets of the 2nd strain (l.h., bb.9–10 & 12; r.h., b.11) can be largely detached.

Source: *Melothesia* (London, 1673). Time signature: 3; the 1st time bars (bb.8a & 16a) are editorial.

Aire

John Blow
(1649–1708)

John Blow, perhaps the most important of Purcell's English contemporaries, was a Gentleman of the Chapel Royal from 1674 and organist of Westminster Abbey from 1668. He relinquished the last-named post in 1679 to make way for his pupil Henry Purcell, but was reinstated after Purcell's death in 1695.

The term *Air* was often borrowed from vocal music to describe a short tuneful instrumental piece. The ornaments and fingering of this *Aire* are not easy, and the piece should be learnt thoroughly in unembellished form first. Mark the syncopation of the figure first stated in b.2 by phrasing it thus: ♪ ♩ ♪

Source: *The Second Book of the Harpsichord Master* (London, 1700). Time signature: 3; b.7, 2nd bass note: *d* not *c*; b.16, 2nd alto note: quaver not crotchet.

Gavot in Gamut

John Blow

Despite the title, this piece, with its lively character, crotchet upbeat and ♩ ♩ syncopations (to be played ♩ ♩), is more like a Bourrée than a Gavotte (it is actually entitled 'Bourrée' in one source). The repeat of the 1st strain (bb.1–4) is notated in full (bb.5–8). The figure ♫ is a written-out slide and can be exaggerated thus: ♫. Suggested phrasing (bb.1–2): ♩ | ♩ ♩ ♩ ♩ ♫ | ♩ ♩ ♩ etc.

Source: *The Second Part of Musick's Hand-maid* (London, 1689). Time signature: 𝄵 ; b.12: ⌄ not ⌄ ; b.15, bass: ♩ ♩ ♩ ; b.20: ornament to 4th, not 5th, treble note.

[Hornpipe]
Z. 667/3

Henry Purcell
(1659–1695)

Purcell ranks alongside William Byrd as one of the greatest of all English composers. In 1679, at the age of only 20, he succeeded his teacher John Blow as organist of Westminster Abbey. Like Mozart and Schubert, he died, tragically, when still only in his thirties.

The *Hornpipe* is a lively English dance of Jig-like character. Stress the first of each group of four quavers thus: ♩♩♩♩. The opening bar might therefore be phrased: ♩. ♪♩♩♩♩♩♩. Since the texture consists of solo and accompaniment, the treble part should be highlighted as if played on a solo instrument.

Source: *A Choice Collection of Lessons for the Harpsichord or Spinnet* (London, 1696). The accidental to the ornament in b.8 is present in the source (placed thus: ⩲).

Prelude
Z. 665/1

Henry Purcell

Almond
Z. 665/2

Henry Purcell

The Prelude and Almond are the first two movements of the *Suit of Lessons* in C, Z.665, which, though of very fine quality, was not included in Purcell's published collection of suites.

The Prelude is of the arpeggiated type in which a richly sonorous effect is created by the sustaining of broken-chordal notes. The pseudo-improvisatory character of the music demands plentiful use of rubato.

'Almond' is an Anglicized form of *Allemande*. Purcell's Allemandes are, in general, quicker and lighter than those of early 18th-century composers: Thomas Mace (*Musick's Monument*, 1676) describes the dance as 'very Ayrey and Lively'. Spread the chords, and perhaps play the quavers with a slight long-short inequality: ♫ = roughly ♪♪ (see Introduction, p. 6). Suggested phrasing (bb.1–3): ♪ ♩. ♫ | ♩ ♩ ♩. ♪ ♩ etc.

Source: *The Second Part of Musick's Hand-maid* (London, 1689). Prelude, b.11, 3rd treble note: dotted quaver not crotchet. Almond, b.11, 2nd bass note: crotchet not quaver; b.24b, l.h.: ♩ ♩ ♩ ; the 1st time bars (bb.12a & 24a) are editorial.

[Suite in G]

1. Tastata [♩ = c. 69]

Bernardo Pasquini
(1637–1710)

2. Corrente [♩ = c. 132]

3. Aria [♩. = *c.* 100]

Bernardo Pasquini, organist of S. Maria in Aracoeli from 1664, was renowned as a keyboard virtuoso. He was the outstanding Italian keyboard composer between Frescobaldi and Domenico Scarlatti.

Pasquini's Suite in G consists of three movements, only one of which (the Corrente) is a dance by name. It is thus quite different in style from the contemporary French suite.

According to its title (from the Italian *tastare*: to touch), the 1st movement is a prelude in which the keys are 'touched' or tried in order to test the tuning of the instrument. The initial chords should be arpeggiated, perhaps in this manner:

Thereafter a contrapuntal texture is established, in which first 8-note and then (from the middle of b.4) 4-note motifs are passed from one part to another.

With regard to the *Corrente*, see the note to Frescobaldi's *Corrente Terza* (p.9). Pasquini's Corrente is, like the 1st movement, a good example of motivic counterpoint: note in particular how the *cambiata* figure of b.6- ♩♩♩♩ -is passed from one part to another in bb.12–14. The 3/2 notation does not imply a slow tempo: imagine instead a lively 3/4: ♩ ♩ ♩ | ♩♩♩♩♩ | etc.

The Aria is equivalent to a *Giga* in the scheme of this suite. Play it with a light touch and at a fairly brisk tempo. Suggested phrasing: ♪♩♩♪|♩ ♪♩♩♪|♩. etc. Imagine the varied groupings of an instrumental ensemble – 1st strain: solo-duet-tutti; 2nd strain: duet-tutti.

Source: London, British Library, Add. 31501, Vol. I. Autograph, dated '6 Maggio 1703' and signed 'Bern^{do} Pasquini'; title crossed out (the title 'Suite in G' is editorial). Upper stave: soprano clef. Key signature: no sharp. Aria: bb.5b & 9a are editorial.

Rigaudon [& Trio]

Georg Böhm
(1661–1733)

Trio. Minore

Rigaudon D.C.

The Lüneburg organist Georg Böhm was one of the most important German composers of the generation immediately before that of Bach. J. S. Bach, according to his son Carl Philipp Emanuel, 'loved and studied the works of Böhm'.

The Rigaudon & Trio are taken from a fine Suite in D, which, though written for the harpsichord, is in the style of a French orchestral suite.

The *Rigaudon* is a folk-dance from southern France which became widely popular in the 17th and early 18th centuries and, according to Mattheson, is associated with sailing and pastoral scenes. Quantz tells us that the Rigaudon is to be played with 'a short and light stroke of the bow'. This remark, which suggests staccato minims and crotchets, is particularly relevant in view of the orchestral style of Böhm's Suite.

In the Rigaudon, the player can imitate the sound of a tutti string ensemble – while the Trio suggests the crisp, precise phrasing of two oboes and bassoon:

In view of the French style of the work, quavers might be played as *notes inégales* (see Introduction, p. 6): unslurred ones long-short (= approx.) and slurred ones short-long (= . or). Spread all r.h. cadential chords (perhaps downwards, as in b.16 of the Trio).

Source: Musikbibliothek der Stadt Leipzig, Ms. III.8.4. (*Andreas Bach Book*). Rigaudon, b.11, last two treble notes: e″ d″. Trio, b.2, last two bass notes: quavers not crotchets.

Bourrée

Johann Caspar Ferdinand Fischer
(c. 1662–1746)

Menuet

Johann Caspar Ferdinand Fischer

Finis

J. C. F. Fischer, Capellmeister at the Baden court, was an important German composer of the same generation as Kuhnau and Böhm. In his keyboard suites, he transferred the style of the French orchestral suite to the keyboard.

The crotchet upbeat and the syncopation in b.6 (played ♩ ♩) of the first of the two pieces are typical of the *Bourrée*, a lively French dance in duple time. The lavish ornamentation of this piece, characteristic of the French style, precludes anything more than a moderately fast tempo. Learn the music without ornaments first, then add them gradually as they become easier to play. Only the shakes to the figure ♩. ♪ in bb. 15, 17 & 21 are absolutely essential. The l.h. ornaments are particularly difficult and could be omitted without detriment to the music.

Phrasing in the Bourrée: ♩ | ♩ ♫ ♩ ♩ | ♫♫ ♩ ♩ | ♩ ♩ ♩ ♫ | ♫♫ ♩ ; bb.17 ff. offer a more legato contrast: ♫♫ | ♩. ♪♩. ♪| ♩. ♪♪ ♩ | ♩ ♩ ♫ ♩ | ♩. ♪♫♫ | ♩. ♪♩. ♪| ♩. . In the Minuet, the square brackets denote hemiola rhythm – play as if in a temporary 2/4: ♩ ♩ | ♩ ♫ | ♩. ♪ (bb.26–7).

The French style of the music suggests that quavers in both movements should be played as *notes inégales* (see Introduction, p. 6): roughly ♩ ♩♪ ♪ etc. Both pieces contain contrasting passages (Bourrée, bb.17–22; Minuet, bb.13–20) that invite the use of a different dynamic. The r.h. chord in bb.1, 7 & 13 of the Minuet might be varied at the repeats by playing ♩. (= ♫ ♩). Closing chords in both movements (e.g. Bourrée, b.16; Minuet, b.12) should be spread – perhaps downwards in the rhythm ♫ ♩ . The sign % in b.21 of the Minuet indicates the *petite reprise*: play from here to the end once again after the repeat of the 2nd half. The last six bars (plus upbeat) of the Bourrée invite similar treatment, though not so marked.

Source: *Musicalisches Blumen-Büschlein* (Augsburg, 1698). Upper stave: soprano clef.

Aria

Johann Kuhnau
(1660–1722)

[Andante ♩= c. 60]

16

Kuhnau was Bach's immediate predecessor as director of music at St Thomas's, Leipzig. His *Clavierübung* ('Keyboard Practice') of 1689 & 1692, from which this Aria is taken, influenced Bach's first publication of the same name: that which contains the six keyboard Partitas (1726–31).

Kuhnau's keyboard suites, unlike Fischer's, are in a native German style, owing far less to French influence. The Aria selected here has the intimate character of the devotional songs that were then sung in the home – the successors of the great Protestant chorales.

Play in an expressive *legato cantabile* style.

Source: *Neuer Clavier Übung: Erster Theil* (Leipzig, 1689). Upper stave: soprano clef.

Gavotte

Johann Kuhnau

The *Gavotte* is a pastoral French dance in moderate 2/2 or ¢ time (despite the time signature C above, think in ¢). Phrases usually begin and end half-way through a bar, and this Gavotte might just as well have been notated: ♩ ♩ | ♩ ♩ ♩ ♫♫ | ♩ ♩ etc.

Suggested phrasing (bb.1–4): ♩ ♩ ♩ ♩ | ♫♫♩ ♩ ♩ | ♩. ♪♪ ♩ ♩ | ♩. ♪♩ :‖ . The continuous quavers of bb.9–12 might be articulated thus: ♫♫ ♫♫ . This phrase, when repeated at the close (bb.13–16), forms the *petite reprise*, which is here written out in full.

Source: *Neuer Clavier Übung, Andrer Theil* (Leipzig, 1692). Upper stave: soprano clef. The repeat of bb.9–12 is indicated by the sign ℅ in b.9.

Menuet

Louis Marchand
(1669–1732)

Marchand was precocious as a child: he was appointed organist of Nevers Cathedral at the age of only 14. As an adult, he was much admired in his own country, France, as an organ virtuoso. He toured Germany from 1713 to 1717 and – so the story goes – failed to appear in a planned contest with J. S. Bach in Dresden.

In Marchand's Minuet in D minor, the inequality (see Introduction, p. 6) is partly notated in the form of dotted quaver rhythms (see bb.11 & 19). This rhythm should be applied to quavers throughout the piece, but perhaps softened in practice to ♩ ♪ ♩ ♪. The slurred pair in b.13 should be played ♪. (or ♪ ♩). Suggested phrasing: ♩ ♩ │♩ ♫ │ ♫♫ │♫♫ .

Source: *Pièces de Clavecin*, Bk I (2nd edn; Paris, 1702). Key signature: no flat; time signature: 3; b.14, 3rd treble note: ⌁ not ⌁ .

Gigue

Charles Dieupart
(*c.* 1667 –*c.* 1740)

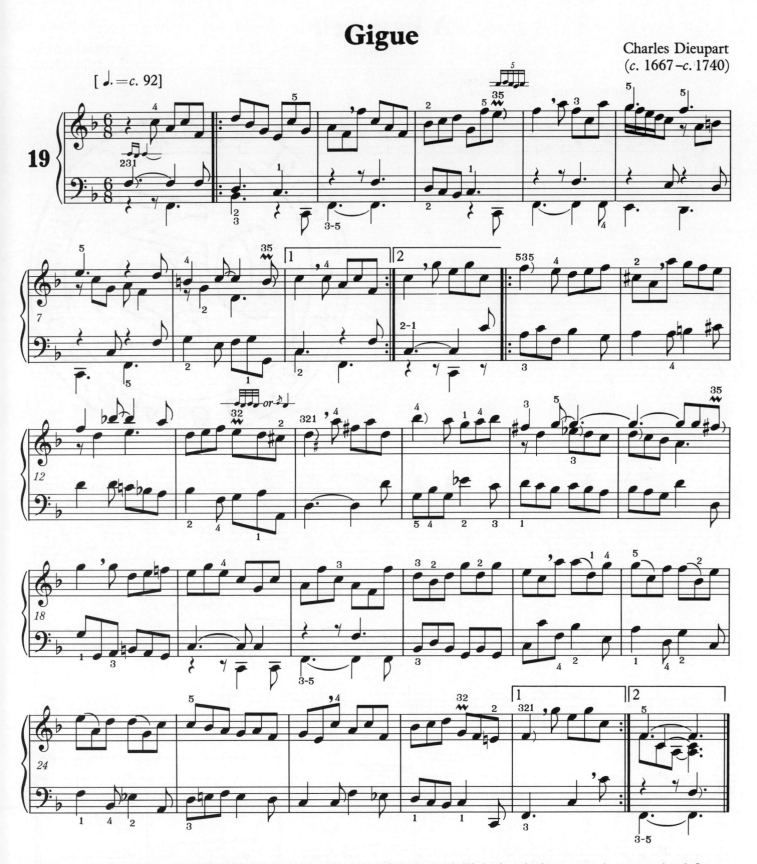

Dieupart was a French composer who spent the last forty years of his life in England. His keyboard suites seem to have exerted an influence on J. S. Bach, who copied out a number of pieces from them.

The French *Gigue* is more complex in texture and more moderate in tempo than the Italian *Giga*. Suggested phrasing: ♪♫♫ | ♫♫ ♫♫ | ♫♪♪ ♫♫ | ♫♫ ♫♫ | ♩ . The slurred quavers in bb.22–4 should perhaps be played ♫. .

Source: *Six Suittes de clavessin* (Amsterdam, 1701).

A Farewell

T 454

Jeremiah Clarke
(c. 1674–1707)

Clarke, a notable contemporary of Purcell's, was a Gentleman of the Chapel Royal and organist – from 1703, also Master of the Choristers – at St. Paul's Cathedral.

This deeply expressive and richly ornamented, Saraband-like piece deserves the most careful study. Add the ornaments as soon as the piece is thoroughly known without them, for they contribute greatly to the expressive power of the music. Suggested phrasing: ♩ ♪ ♩♩ ♩♩♩ ♩ ♩ | ♩♩ ♩ ♩♩ | ♩ . Sharpen the dotted crotchet rhythms (as in b.3) throughout to ♩.. ♪ . The figure ♫ in b.5 is a written-out slide: play ♫. . In the closing bar of each half, hold down all notes for the length of the bar. Accelerate slightly into the long shakes in bb.20 & 24. The last phrase (bb.21, 2nd crotchet – 25) forms a written-out *petite reprise* (short repeated passage at the close) – cf. bb.17–21 – and might be played at a reduced dynamic level.

Source: *The Third Book of the Harpsichord Master* (London, 1702). B.25b, r.h.: 3rd too high. The suggestion for the 2nd time in the l.h. of b.9 is editorial.

Saraband

William Croft
(1678–1727)

William Croft was a chorister and later organist at the Chapel Royal. In 1708 he succeeded his teacher John Blow as organist of Westminster Abbey.

This Saraband, which should be only moderately slow, exhibits throughout the 2nd-beat stress that has become the best-known feature of the dance. Spread all 3-note r.h. chords and sharpen the rhythm ♩. ♪ to ♩.. ♪ .

Source: *A Choice Collection of Ayres for the harpsichord or spinett* (London, 1700). Title: Sarabrand; key signature: two flats; no time signature.

Jigg

John Barrett
(*c.* 1676–*c.* 1719)

Barrett was a pupil of John Blow's who became master at Christ's Hospital, London and organist of St Mary-at-Hill.

The *Jig* is an English forerunner of the French *Gigue*. The lively 6/8 time and the dotted rhythms of bb.7–8 and 17 ff. are characteristic of this dance. Use a very light touch. Suggested phrasing:

Source: *The Second Book of the Harpsichord Master* (London, 1700). B.24, bass, 4th quaver: crotchet rest not quaver rest.

New Aire

Anon.

It is not known who composed this fine Bourrée-like piece, but note the skilful way in which the first three treble notes of b.10 (phrasing perhaps ♩ ♩ ♩) are taken up in sequence in bb.13–14 and, in a different form, in bb.21–2 (♩ ♩ ♩ | ♩ ♩ ♩). Note also the treble-bass imitation in bb.19–20 and the seemingly inevitable manner in which the opening phrase of the piece does duty also as the closing phrase. Suggested phrasing (bb.1–5): ♩ ♩ ♩ ♩ ♩ ♩ ♩ | ♩. ♩ ♩ ♩ ♩ ♩ ♩ | ♩. ♩ ♩ ♩ ♩ etc. The dotted rhythm in b.13 suggests that the parallel figures in the preceding and following bars should also be dotted.

Source: *The Harpsichord Master* (London, 1697). B.15, 2nd alto note: minim not crotchet; b.24b, treble & tenor: semibreve; bass: minim.

[Marche]

Johann Christoph Graupner
(1683–1760)

Graupner was Capellmeister at the court of Darmstadt. Like his friend Telemann, he was an extremely prolific composer, but very little of his music is widely known (or even available) today, despite its attractiveness.

This piece is a rondeau with three episodes (starting at the upbeats to bb.17, 33 & 49), so that the overall structure is ABACADA. Use a contrasting dynamic or manual in the episodes. Suggested phrasing (bb.1–4):  . In bb.59–61, harmony notes have been added by the editor in small print: it was often left to the performer to add such inner parts in the Baroque period. The same applies to ornamentation: the original of this piece contains no ornaments, for the player would have been expected to improvise them. Here, an optional editorial scheme of ornaments is provided in small print.

Source: Darmstadt, Hessische Landes- und Hochschulbibliothek, Mus. ms. 1231. Upper stave: soprano clef.

Gavotte en Rondeau

Georg Philipp Telemann
(1681–1767)

Telemann was, from 1721 until his death, director of music at the five principal churches in Hamburg and Cantor at the Johanneum. An extremely prolific composer, he was among the most important of Bach's German contemporaries.

The *Gavotte* is a pastoral French dance in moderate 2/2 or ¢ time, with phrases beginning and ending half-way through the bar. Telemann's Gavotte in D minor takes the form of a rondeau: repeats of the opening rondeau theme (bb.1–10) alternate with two episodes (starting half-way through bb.10 & 22), giving rise to the overall structure ABACA. As a rule, crotchets should be detached, but mixed phrasing is needed in bb.7–9 and parallels – ♩ ♩ | ♩ ♩ etc. – and in the 1st episode: ♩♩♩♩ | ♩♩♩♩ ♩ ♩ | ♩ ♩ .

Source: *Der getreue Music-Meister* (Hamburg, 1728). Upper stave: soprano clef; time signature: 𝄵 .

Air

Johann Mattheson
(1681–1764)

Mattheson, a friend of Handel's ,was from 1715 to 1728 director of music at Hamburg Cathedral. He was a fine organist and a prolific writer on music as well as a composer.

The title 'Air' ('tune' or 'song') is particularly appropriate in view of the lyrical, *cantabile* character of the treble part. Phrasing will be predominantly in short legato groups: ♩♩ ♩ ♪ | ♫♫♫ ♪ | ♫♫♫ ♫♫♫ | ♩♩ ♩ . The falling 5th figure of b.5 recurs frequently, sometimes (as in bb.8 & 10) as a falling 3rd: the authentic slur in b.20 shows how it should be phrased. The closing phrase of the 1st half (b.14, 5th quaver) introduces a livelier figure that is carried over into the 2nd half: ♩♪ | ♩♫♫ ♩ ♩ . Spread the final chord of each half.

Source: *Pièces de Clavecin* (London, 1714). Half-bar rests (bb.1, 17 & 27–9): ▬ ; triplets (bb.18 & 31): ▦ .

Menuet

Gottfried Heinrich Stölzel
(1690–1749)

Menuet-Trio

BWV 929

Johann Sebastian Bach
(1685–1750)

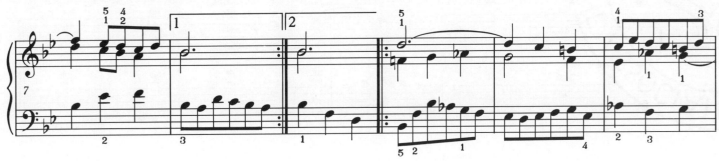

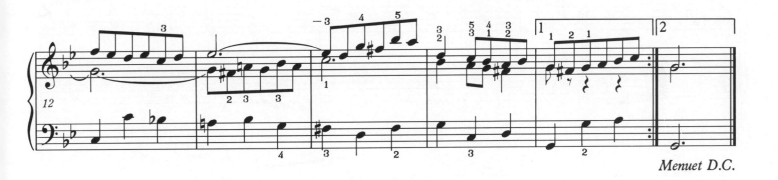

Menuet D.C.

Stölzel was Capellmeister successively at the courts of Gera and Saxe-Gotha. He had a wide reputation as a composer in his day.

The Minuet is taken from a Partita in G minor which Bach's eldest son, Wilhelm Friedemann, then aged about 12, copied into his *Clavierbüchlein* ('Little Keyboard Book'). His father contributed a composition of his own as Trio to Stölzel's Minuet.

Imagine tutti strings in the Minuet and a contrasting group of two oboes and bassoon in the Trio. Suggested phrasing in the Minuet (bb.1–5 etc.): ♩ ♫♫♩ ♩ ♫♫♩ ♩ ♩ ♩ ♩ ♩ ♩ ♩ ♩ ♩ ♩ ♩ etc. Spread all chords of four notes or more. The ornaments and the harmony notes in small print are editorial.

The Trio is in three contrapuntal parts throughout. Look out for suspensions, which should be accented and slurred like appoggiaturas; thus treble, bb.2–3: ♩ ♩ ♩ ♩ ♫♫♩ ; bass, bb.5–6: ♩ ♩ ♩ ; and treble, bb.9–10: ♩ ♩ ♩ ♩ . The treble-alto imitation in bb.5–6 & 13–14 should be phrased in twos: ♫♫♫♩ .

Source: *Clavier-Büchlein vor Wilhelm Friedemann Bach* (Cöthen, from 1720). Minuet, b.17, bass, beats 1–2: ♩ ♩ (line-change between the two notes; tie missing); b.28, treble: dotted minim; the 1st time bar, b.32a, is editorial.

Menuet

BWV 818 a/5

Johann Sebastian Bach

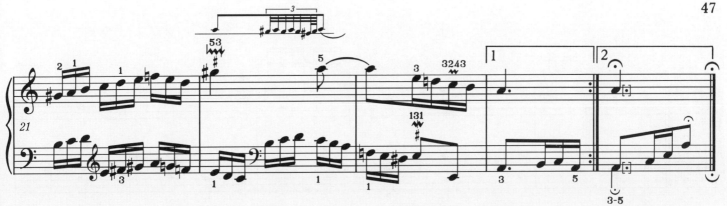

Bach is often considered a conservative composer, but he was in fact capable of writing in a variety of different styles, both ancient and modern. His florid style, as exemplified in this Minuet, is both highly personal and very advanced for its day. And his later suites represent the final stage in a process that lasted throughout the Baroque period, in which simple dances were gradually transformed into highly sophisticated works of art. The piece selected here, for example (from the revised version of the Suite in A minor, BWV 818), is among the most elaborate of Bach's Minuets and might be described as a character piece in Minuet time rather than a Minuet proper.

Play in an expressive *legato cantabile* style, executing the ornaments on long notes slowly and melodically.

Sources: Musikbibliothek der Stadt Leipzig, Ms.8 (Fasc.23); W. Berlin, Staatsbibliothek Preussischer Kulturbesitz, Mus. ms. Bach P 804 (Fasc.36).

Minuet
HWV 434/4

George Frideric Handel
(1685–1759)

Handel's keyboard music is of minor importance compared with his operas and oratorios, but it is of consistently high quality and includes a great deal of attractive music.

This grand Minuet from Handel's 2nd collection of suites, with its giant leaps, shows his melodic writing at its boldest. Phrase the melody in such a way as to lean strongly on the appoggiatura at the beginning of bb.2 & 4: ♩ ♩ ♪|♩ ♩ ♩ etc. The broken-chordal notes in the l.h. should perhaps be held down throughout the bar. The square brackets in bb.14–15 indicate hemiola – imagine a temporary 2/4: ♩. ♪|♩. ♪| ♩ ♪♩|.

Source: *Suites de Pièces* (London, *c*.1733). Bb.11 & 14 and throughout 2nd half: ⁓ not ⁓. Bb.27–8 wrongly placed between bb.24 & 25. Treble quavers in b.31 a tone too low. Shake in b.37 to 3rd, not 4th, treble note.

Air

HWV 464

George Frideric Handel

This piece is Handel's own keyboard version of the famous Air (i.e. tune) from the *Water Music*.

The notation is – as often in Handel – inconsistent: all equally notated rhythms should be assimilated to the prevailing unequal, dotted rhythm, so that ⁊ ♫♫ (b.1 etc.) = ⁊ ♫♩ and ♪♪ (b.17) = ♩: ♪ . But having done that, it is advisable, in view of the calm serenity of the music, to soften all dotted rhythms to ♩ ♪ . The dot was a variable quantity in the Baroque period, and players were expected to sharpen dotted rhythms where greater vigour was required and soften them in quieter, more relaxed moods.

All 3-note r.h. chords should be spread (perhaps downwards in bb.8 & 18 and upwards elsewhere).

Source: Cambridge, Fitzwilliam Museum, 30.H.10 (autograph).

Menuet

Gottlieb Muffat
(1690–1770)

Gottlieb Muffat, son of the equally famous composer Georg Muffat (1653-1704), was a pupil of Fux's. He became court organist in Vienna and was the leading Viennese keyboard composer in the early 18th century. Handel admired him enough to borrow extensively from his suites, and the Minuet selected here is more familiar in Handel's adaptation in his Concerto grosso in D, Op.6 No.5.

Vertical strokes, as in the l.h. of b.4, mean simply staccato. Slanting strokes through chords, as in b.8, denote a rising arpeggio (spread in the rhythm ♪♪♪ ♩). Muffat uses the sign ♯ᵕ to signify a mordent with a sharpened lower auxiliary. The sign 𝄋 in b.17 indicates that the last eight bars are to be played again after the repeat of the 2nd half, forming the so-called *petite reprise*.

Source: *Componimenti Musicali per il cembalo* (Augsburg, *c*.1739). Upper stave: soprano clef.

La Bourbonnoise

Gavotte

François Couperin
(1668–1733)

François Couperin, one of the greatest French composers of the Baroque period, was, like J. S. Bach, the outstanding member of a large family of musicians. He was appointed royal harpsichordist in 1717.

La Bourbonnoise is, like most of Couperin's harpsichord pieces, descriptive: it is a musical portrait of a female pupil – daughter of the Duc de Bourbon. It is also a typical *Gavotte*, with its moderate 2/2 time and its half-bar openings and closes. The piece is built on the standard Baroque bass that Bach used in the Goldberg Variations (cf. also Froberger's Sarabande in F, Bk 2, p.14 and d'Anglebert's Menuet in G, Bk 3, p.15).

The profuse ornamentation should be added after the piece has been learnt in unembellished form. Play the quavers as *notes inégales* (see Introduction, p. 6): ♩♩♩♩ = roughly ♩ ♪♩ ♪ . Closing r.h. chords (bb.8 & 16) should be spread (perhaps downwards in the rhythm ♫♩ ♩).

Source: *Pièces de Clavecin*, Bk I (Paris, 1713). Time signature: 2; the slurs take the form ⌐¬ .

La Flateuse
Rondeau

Jean-François Dandrieu
(*c.* 1682–1738)

Dandrieu was, from 1721, organist at the royal chapel in Paris. After Couperin and Rameau, he was the most celebrated French harpsichord composer of the 18th century.

La Flateuse – The Flattering [Girl] – has become well known under the false attribution to Purcell. It was formerly entitled *La Légère* – The Fickle [Girl].

The piece takes the form of a *Gavotte en rondeau*: the rondeau theme (bb.1–8) is repeated after each *couplet* or episode, giving rise to the overall structure ABACA. Suggested phrasing of the rondeau theme: ♩ ♩ | ♩♩♩ ♩ ♩ | ♩. ♩♩♩ ; and of the 1st episode: ♩♩♩ | ♩ ♩ ♩♩ | ♩ ♩ ♩ | ♩ ♩ ♩ | ♩ ♩ . Quavers should be paired in *notes inégales* (♫ = approx. ♩₃♪ ; see Introduction, p. 6), except for the broken-chordal ones in the l.h. of the 1st episode, which remain equal. Closing r.h. chords (bb.8 & 16) should be spread (perhaps downwards).

Source: *Troisième Livre de Pièces de Clavecin* (Paris, 1734). Time signature: 2. In the source, the piece is followed by two variations.

Menuet

Jean-Philippe Rameau
(1683–1764)

34

2^e **Menuet**

Rameau was, alongside Couperin, one of the greatest French composers of the 18th century. His keyboard works are among the boldest and most original products of the French classical school of harpsichord music.

The two Minuets are to be played *alternativement*: that is to say, the 1st Minuet should be played again (without repeats) after the 2nd, giving rise to an overall ABA structure. Note that the repeat of the 1st strain in both Minuets is written out in full, for the l.h. part is played down an 8ve the second time (see b.9 in each case). Quavers should be played as *notes inégales* throughout (♩♩ = roughly ♩₃♪; see Introduction, p. 6).

Minuet II offers a tonic minor contrast to Minuet I. Note also the different accentuation of their themes: predominantly off-beat phrasing in Minuet I – ♫♩ │♩♩♩│♩♩♫♩│♩♩ │♩♩♩│♩♩♩ etc. (2nd strain: ♫♩ │♩♩♩) – contrasts with on-the-beat phrasing in Minuet II: ♫♩ │♩ │♩♩♩│♩ │♫♩│♩. │♪♪♪ etc.

Source: *Nouvelles Suites de Pièces de Clavecin* (Paris, *c*.1728). Time signature: 3. Minuet II, bb.2–3, l.h.: ties to *g*'s (b.2, beats 2–3; b.3, beats 1–2) in place of slurs (corr. here by analogy with bb.10–11); b.10, l.h., 3rd crotchet: 3rd lower (*e* flat/*g* not *g*/*b* flat).

L'Amusante
Rondeau

Louis-Claude Daquin
(1694–1772)

Daquin was very precocious as a child, holding organist's posts in Paris from the age of 12. In 1739 he was appointed *organiste du roi* (royal organist). He was widely regarded as the finest French keyboard player of his generation.

The title *L'Amusante* – The Entertaining [Girl/Piece] – and the expression mark *tendrement* (tenderly) sufficiently indicate the character of this music. The piece is cast in the form of a rondeau with two episodes, or *couplets,* the overall structure being ABACA (the sign ℅ indicates a repeat of the opening rondeau theme, bb.1–13). *Notes inégales* are inappropriate in this piece owing to the broken-chordal character of the l.h. quavers. In the words 'nottes très liées' (notes very slurred), the composer informs us that this l.h. part is to be played *molto tenuto* – ♩♩♩♩ | ♩♩♩♩♩ ♩ – creating a rich, warm harmonic background. Editorial square brackets above the stave denote hemiola rhythm: articulate in minim groups, giving the effect of a temporary 2/4; thus (bb.23–5): ♩. ♪| ♩. ♪| ♩. ♪| ♩ . Spread all closing r.h. chords, as in b.13 (perhaps downwards).

Source: *Ier Livre de Pièces de Clavecin* (Paris, 1735). Time signature: 3. Only Part I is given here; Part II of *L'Amusante* is a rondeau in E.

Minuet

Jean-Baptiste Loeillet
(1680–1730)

Loeillet, a member of a Flemish family of musicians, settled in London in about 1705, where he made a successful career for himself and became known as 'John Loeillet of London'.

The elegant theme, which might be phrased thus ♩ ♩ | ♩♪♩ ♩ | ♩ ♩ ♪ | ♩ ♩ is stated twice in the 1st half of the piece and briefly alluded to in the first four bars of the 2nd half. Thereafter it does not recur, for the 2nd 'half', which is almost twice as long as the 1st, consists of a succession of new themes. In bb.26–7, the square brackets denote hemiola rhythm – articulate in minim groups, ignoring the barline; thus: ♩♪♩ ♩ ♪♩ ♪ . The r.h. of bb.29 ff. can be enhanced by using *tenuto* touch: ♩♪♪♪♪♪ | ♪♪♪♪♪♪ | ♪♪♪♪♪ etc. In bb.39–40, shorten the 1st note to throw the accent on the 2nd: ♩ ♩ | ♩ ♩ | .

Source: *Six Suits of Lessons for the Harpsicord or Spinnet* (London, *c.* 1723).

Sonata
Kp.453

Domenico Scarlatti
(1685–1757)

Domenico Scarlatti, son of the famous Alessandro, was the greatest Italian keyboard composer of the 18th century. He moved to Portugal in 1719 and, nine years later, settled in Spain, where he cultivated a boldly original keyboard style.

The Sonata in A, Kp.453 is notable for its classical grace and elegance. The opening r.h. figure might be phrased thus: ♪♪♩ ♩ | ♩. ; and the variant in bb.11–12: ♪♪♪♩ ♩ | ♩ ♩ ♩ . The crotchet chords in bb.23–4 and the like should be slurred – ♪♪♩ ♩ ♩ – but elsewhere crotchets will mostly be detached.

Source: Münster II 52. Key signature: two sharps.

AB 2087

Gavotta

Thomas Augustine Arne
(1710–1778)

Arne was one of the most notable English composers of the 18th century and possessed striking melodic gifts. He is best known for his stage works and songs, but his keyboard works contain much attractive music.

Arne here uses the Italian term *Gavotta*, for the piece is Italianate in style and belongs to a sonata rather than to a French suite. It illustrates the transition, at the end of the Baroque period, from binary dance form to sonata form: the dominant-key group begins in b.8, the development after the double bar, and the recapitulation in b.40; the dominant group returns in the home key in b.48.

Suggested phrasing of the main theme: ♩♩|♩ ♩ |♫♪'♩♩|♩ ♫♫♫♫|♩ .Most four-quaver groups can be articulated as in the theme (♫♫). The trill theme (bb.8 ff.) might be played with staccato quavers: ♩ ♫♫ ♩ etc. In the l.h. of bb.22-3, the quaver groups begin on the 4th and 8th quavers of the bar: ♪|♪♪♪♪ ♪♪♪♪| ; in the r.h. of bb.25 & 27, on the 2nd and 6th: |♪♫♫♫ ♫♫♫|♫ ♫ . The occasional l.h. shakes can be omitted without detriment to the music if they prove too difficult.

Source: *VIII Sonatas or Lessons for the Harpsichord* (London, 1756). B.26, 4th treble note: quaver *e''* flat appoggiatura, not *tr.*

Air

HWV 464

George Frideric Handel

This piece is Handel's own keyboard version of the famous Air (i.e. tune) from the *Water Music*.

The notation is – as often in Handel – inconsistent: all equally notated rhythms should be assimilated to the prevailing unequal, dotted rhythm, so that ♪♩♩♪ (b.1 etc.) = ♪ ♩♩♪ and ♪♪ (b.17) = ♪. ♪ . But having done that, it is advisable, in view of the calm serenity of the music, to soften all dotted rhythms to ♩ ♪. The dot was a variable quantity in the Baroque period, and players were expected to sharpen dotted rhythms where greater vigour was required and soften them in quieter, more relaxed moods.

All 3-note r.h. chords should be spread (perhaps downwards in bb.8 & 18 and upwards elsewhere).

Source: Cambridge, Fitzwilliam Museum, 30.H.10 (autograph).

ELEGY AND TOCCATA

for

VIOLIN and PIANO

by

LENNOX BERKELEY

Op. 33, Nos. 2 and 3

CHESTER MUSIC

For Frederick Grinke

ELEGY

FOR VIOLIN AND PIANO

LENNOX BERKELEY

CH 00395

April 1950

For Frederick Grinke

TOCCATA

FOR VIOLIN AND PIANO

LENNOX BERKELEY

CH 00395

For Frederick Grinke

ELEGY

FOR VIOLIN AND PIANO

LENNOX BERKELEY

CH 00395

For Frederick Grinke

TOCCATA

FOR VIOLIN AND PIANO

LENNOX BERKELEY

CH 00395